301·31
HUN
×26876

Man's Environment and
the Atlantic

by
James R. Huntley

70871448.

June 1971
NATO Information Service
1110 Brussels

Mr. James R. Huntley is an American author
and consultant on International Affairs.

TABLE OF CONTENTS

TWENTY MONTHS OF APRIL :
THE GENESIS OF AN IDEA

> *The North Atlantic Council has established a Committee on the Challenges of Modern Society to consider problems of the human environment.*
>
> NATO Press Communique,
> 6 November 1969

THE idea had grown from a seed planted more than twenty years earlier. On the fourth of April 1949, on a mahogany table in a government building in Washington, the historic North Atlantic Treaty was signed. Twelve* nations of Europe and North America bound themselves through the Treaty to consider an armed attack against one as an attack against all. In a spare document of barely four pages, a political framework was created around which an unprecedented collective force for peace has been established.

The bulk of the North Atlantic Treaty concerned the threat of war and the means of resolving international disputes. But the framers included one short Article, the second, which may in the end overshadow all the others. Article 2 declared :

> The Parties will contribute toward the further development of peaceful and friendly international relations by strengthening their free institutions, by bringing about a better understanding of the principles upon which these institutions are founded, and by promoting conditions of stability and well-being. They will seek to eliminate conflict in their international economic policies and will encourage economic collaboration between any or all of them.

More than nine Aprils passed before the North Atlantic Council — the highest authority of the Alliance —

* Three — Greece, Turkey, and the Federal Republic of Germany — joined NATO later.

could turn its attention to Article 2; in May 1956, the Council set up a Committee of Three on Non-Military-Co-operation. The Committee told the Council in December that NATO must become more than a military alliance, and recommended a wide range of political, economic, cultural, and other forms of civil co-operation. These recommendations led to the setting up of several specialised committees, including one on Science.

Scientific co-operation progressed dramatically ; more than 30,000 scientists from NATO and non-NATO nations have, for example, participated in NATO-sponsored Advanced Study Institutes. Visiting professorships, fellowships, and other forms of co-operation in the social sciences and humanities developed in a cultural programme.

Most important, over the years NATO's political capacity improved until, in 1967, the Alliance could formally recognize its second main function, equal in importance to its first, the maintenance of military strength and political solidarity to deter aggression. NATO's "second dimension" was "to pursue the search for progress towards a more stable relationship in which the underlying political issues" preventing an accommodation in Europe "can be solved". In short, NATO had become the principal means whereby the Allies were to develop and promote a policy of détente and agreement with the USSR and its partners.

NATO's Third Dimension

Implicit in the nascent scientific, cultural and other non-military activities of the Alliance, and in the broad language of Article 2 of the Treaty, was yet a third dimension. And on the twentieth anniversary of the Treaty, rapid social evolution in the NATO countries impelled the President of the United States, Mr.

Nixon, to articulate a bold proposal in this direction. To the Foreign Ministers of the Allies, gathered again in Washington on 10 April 1969, he declared his conviction that "the alliance of the West... needs a social dimension, to deal with our concern for the quality of life in this final third of the twentieth century." The President urged NATO action, explaining that :

> We are all advanced societies, sharing the benefits and the gathering torments of a rapidly advancing industrial technology. The industrial nations share no challenge more urgent than that of bringing 20th century man and his environment to terms with one another — of making the world fit for man, and helping man learn how to remain in harmony with his rapidly changing world.

The Foreign Ministers agreed to explore the idea, and in November established a Committee on the Challenges of Modern Society (CCMS), under the North Atlantic Council. They directed CCMS to:

> examine how to improve, in every practical way, the exchange of views and experience among the Allied countries in the task of creating a better environment for their societies.. and to consider specific problems of the human environment with the deliberate objective of stimulating action by member governments.

The CCMS Programme Launched

Discussion and planning followed. How should the new Committee work ? How could it make a distinctive contribution in a field — "the Environment" — which was rapidly becoming the objective of a number of international organizations ? What unique methods, drawn out of NATO'S special experience, could be brought to bear on broad social and ecological issues ?

How NATO has answered these and related questions is the subject of this booklet.

By the twenty-second April of NATO's existence — in 1971 — the Alliance had already established itself firmly as a catalyst for environmental action. Before we review the work of CCMS, perhaps it would first be wise to ask: What is the "environment problem"? And why must it be seen — at least in part — as an *international* problem?

SHAPING THE HUMAN ENVIRONMENT:
AN INTERNATIONAL CHALLENGE

> *It is the paradox of our times that the very progress achieved by man in the technological and social fields originally intended to improve his way of living, now poses challenges to present and future generations.*
>
> Manlio Brosio,
> Secretary General of the
> North Atlantic Treaty Organization.

THE survival of human society as we know it — perhaps the survival of Man himself as a species — is threatened now by a new factor : the rapid deterioration of the globe itself as an ecological system.

Ecology — the study of the relationship between life forms and their environment — was until only yesterday a little noticed, esoteric discipline of chiefly academic interest. Ecologists pondered over the totality of living things in a copse, for example, or around a pond, or in some exotic bit of land in, say, the sub-Arctic wastes.

But in the last years of the 1960s the perspective of the ecologist, who looks at an "ecosystem" as a whole, has been absorbed by other scientists, city planners, politicians, and public administrators, and projected onto a world-wide plane. First by a few, then by significantly larger numbers of the general public, the balance of the entire planet and its future as a home for Man, has been seen to be at stake.

The world-wide ecological crisis (for crisis it is) has three main components : urbanisation, now a universal phenomenon ; the population explosion ; and the damaging encroachment of man's technologies on his physical and socio-cultural environments.

As technological innovation takes over in agriculture, the farm population (and especially in the industrialized countries) has moved inexorably into urban areas. In turn, the impact of headlong urbanization is compounded by the rising curve of population growth : unless curbed, the planet's population could well stand at six times its present level of 3½ billion, by the year 2080.

Add to urbanization and burgeoning population the full force of the "technological revolution", which has with dramatic suddenness given rise to unprecedented forces of change, and one has the components of a global crisis. The only truly incredible fact in this "mix" is that Man, in his parochialism and haste to go about his daily business, didn't recognize the crisis sooner.

Some Indicators

Here are just a few random examples of the breakdown in the global ecosystem :

1. The overall loudness of the noise environment in advanced countries is doubling every ten years. The pain threshold is about 140 decibels (db), but prolonged exposure to lower intensities can have severe physiological and aesthetic consequences. Rock bands produce readings between 100 and 120 db, compared with 140 db for some jet planes, 130 db for pneumatic riveters. A German study has shown abnormal heart rhythms among steelworkers continuously exposed to severe noise; an Italian study of weavers, similarly exposed, has shown abnormal brain wave patterns, suggestive in some cases of personality disorders.

2. An estimated 40 million fish died suddenly in the summer of 1969, when a barrel of lethal chemicals was inadvertently dropped in the Rhine near Koblenz. The public effect was electric, all along the multi-

nation banks of the Rhine. But these same populations had paid little attention to an earlier warning from the Council of Europe, whose figures showed that the Rhine, especially in its lower reaches, is normally little more than an open sewer. A count showed 30-100 harmful bacteria per millilitre of water in Switzerland, rising to 2,000 by the time the river had reached the Lake of Constance, 24,000 at Bonn and, as the Rhine flowed into Holland, a count of 100,000 per millilitre.

3. Significant lead contamination, probably mostly from lead alkyls used in automobile fuel, is now worldwide. Data obtained from analysis of snow cores on northern Greenland have shown the following trend for particulate lead :

From 800 B.C. to 1750 A.D. — an increase from 0 to 0.005/ug/kg

From 1750 to 1940 — an increase to 0.065/ug/kg

From 1940 to 1952 — an increase to 0.25/ug/kg

4. Traffic casualties have been described as "an epidemic spreading around the world". In NATO countries alone, the annual deaths in traffic exceeded 111,000 in one year (1965-66).

5. One hundred and fifty types of birds and animals have become extinct through human agency. Approximately 1,000 species are considered to be rare or endangered.

6. The atmosphere has been described as a sink for some 12 billion tons of carbon dioxide released yearly by our industrial civilisation. About half of this remains in the air permanently. By the year 2000 the amount of CO_2 is expected to have increased by 25 %. Normally CO_2 has been an integral part of the earth's regenerative processes, but scientists say that increasingly abnormal amounts could change the world's climate significantly. The precise effect is still uncertain, but conceivably a movement of sev-

eral degrees in the average temperature of the earth's atmosphere is possible. This may sound insignificant, but the last Ice Age resulted from an average temperature drop of around 8° C.

The list could of course be extended indefinitely ; everyone who reads his newspapers or watches TV can add his own disconcerting statistics. The full dimensions of the crisis are as yet unknown ; it will require several years of study — and particularly the organization of an effective network of international co-operation — before the essential facts can be gathered on a regular and complete basis.

But there is no question that a crisis exists... a crisis which ultimately could prove as significant for Man as the questions of peace and war, or race relations. For the quality of life, and perhaps ultimately even the *possibility* of life, for all human beings is at stake.

Why is this an International Crisis ?

For some decades, to be sure, local and national authorities in most countries have been dealing with such obvious problems as the contamination of water and, more recently, air pollution. Yet even if local action is forceful and well-considered, it cannot always be effective. For the winds, the oceans, and many rivers know no national boundaries. Pesticides used on the fields of India, or Denmark, or California can — and do — find their way through the air and the seas to such far-away places as Antarctica.

In recent years, a curious red snow has fallen at times on parts of Norway ; chemical analysis traced the particles to factory emissions in such distant places as the Ruhr and the British Isles.

The Great Lakes — especially Erie and Ontario — are in danger of "dying" unless the process of eutrophication is stopped and reversed. But it can only be done if the United States and Canada, both of which border the two lakes, can jointly agree on the necessary measures, jointly put them into effect, and jointly pay for them.

In such a densely populated and developed an area as Northwestern Europe, with several countries linked tightly by geography and economics, the need for common regulations and enforcement procedures to control various forms of pollution — for example, in the Rhine River — seems evident. Many planners and scientists believe these countries must go even further, and develop common strategies for the use and development of their precious land.

In a remarkable report to the Economic and Social Council of the UN (in May 1969), the Secretary General of the UN portrayed the extraordinary world-wide dangers to man's environment. He said :

> It has become clear that we all live in one biosphere within which space and resources, though vast, are limited.

He then proposed, and the General Assembly agreed, to hold an International Conference on Human Environment, in Stockholm in June 1972. There is agreement among the members of the United Nations that the environment issue deserves important consideration on a world-wide level, but there is not yet agreement in that diverse forum as to *how important* the issue is.

Among the industrialized nations, most of whom are members of NATO, public concern for the environment issue has mounted more rapidly than in other parts of the world. And it is understandable that this should be so.

The Ecological Crisis in Advanced Nations

Public consciousness of any important new international problem tends to develop gradually, unless there is a major disaster or threat of general war. So it is now surprising that even though the environmental crisis is obviously a matter of capital significance for the entire world, the great mass of the public, world-wide, is only dimly aware of it as yet.

The consciousness — indeed a sense of alarm — has arisen first in those countries which are "ahead" in what has come to be known as the process of "development". First and foremost among these is the United States, which began the economic and social transformations of the Industrial Revolution a decade or two behind several European countries, yet rushed ahead in the 1950's and 1960's into still another stage in modernization, called by some "post-industrial", and others "technetronic" society. It is in the United States that the automobile first became the indispensable companion of virtually every family, with far-reaching effects on patterns of land-use, social mores, and the quality of air. Commercial aircraft, television and other forms of high-speed communication, "throw-away" products, computers, and synthetic drugs — each one the product of the accelerating technological revolution — all came into widespread use in the United States first.

These innovations are producing deep changes in the way men live the world over, but above all in Canada and Western Europe, where development has closely followed that of the United States, so accelerating in the past two decades that it is perhaps not inaccurate to speak of an emerging "trans-Atlantic technological society", with more common problems, as well as common prospects, than ever before in history.

This new dimension in trans-Atlantic interdependence was explained in a slightly different way by Dr. Daniel P. Moynihan, President Nixon's Adviser on Urban Affairs, when in 1969 he addressed the first meeting of NATO's Committee on the Challenges of Modern Society :

The changing ecological balance is something that mankind has never had to deal with before. This is new. It is different. This fact is indispensable to understanding the particular challenge before us. The newest dimension of freedom arises in the context of advancing technology. More accurately, it arises *from* advancing technology. First, the folk technology of the early industrial revolution and later the ever-mounting and more systematic application of scientific knowledge to practical problems has created an almost world-wide vision of societies of material plenty in which individual men become all they are capable of being. Personal liberty and democratic government would be the pre-condition of such societies, but their unique achievement would be measured by the degree to which men and women comprising them live large, creative and fulfilling lives. And this is a very large vision indeed. The difficulty with it is that it exists in the context of time constraints that make it, for a vision, at once so powerful and extraordinarily fragile. This is so.. .because technology that created it only hours ago in the history of mankind, threatens to destroy it only hours from now. In the past we have seen individual liberties suppressed and later revived; we have seen political liberties destroyed only to be restored undiminished by that experience. But the changing ecological balance of mankind in terms of the chemical nature of the universe, in terms of the size of the population of the universe, is such that the disasters that are upon us can become irreversible, just as the opportunities are unprecedented. And this is the issue which we bring to this Council table.

It is not necessarily surprising or unusual that the United States should be the first nation to raise the environment issue in NATO, or for that matter in the Organization for Economic Co-operation and Development or in the United Nations. For the United States is simply the first nation — but by no means the last — to be confronted with the hard realities of the world ecological crisis. It is thus not at all strange that the Americans should want to warn their Canadian and European allies, seek their help, and offer advice born of brief but bitter experience with the forces of environmental deterioration.

Nor is it strange that NATO's members, comprising the larger part of the developed world, should feel a collective impulse, in advance of other nations, to "do something" about the environmental crisis.

WHAT IS NATO DOING
IN THE ENVIRONMENT FIELD ?

THE chapter which follows lookt at NATO's immediate efforts to help its members meet the challenges of modern society. There are special difficulties which all international organizations face — problems of differing languages, a sometimes inconvenient layering of machinery over and beyond national structures, and inevitable delays in securing agreement and approval among a number of national authorities. If one takes obstacles of this kind into account, then the amount which CCMS has accomplished since December 1969, when it began its work, and the significant prospects which are already in sight, are indeed striking.

Action to Stop Oil Spills

As the world's consumption of oil has risen dramatically in the past decade, as leviathan tankers have been introduced, and as intensive drilling for oil has begun at sea in various places, public concern for increasing discharges of oil — intentional as well as accidental — has risen.

Because NATO's members wished to direct their new environmental programme towards matters of urgent concern which lend themselves readily to action, oil spills received early priority.

CCMS activites are organized by individual member countries of NATO, each acting as a "pilot". Belgium took on the problem of oil spills, as a first step in the broader project of open waters pollution. In just six months, defying all normal expectations, the Belgian Government convened an international conference on oil spills. The experts (from NATO countries as well as Spain and from other international organizations) analysed the problem and made their recommendations. One month later, in December 1970, NATO's Foreign Ministers acted.

The heart of their action was a commitment by all members to work urgently to eliminate intentional discharges of oil and oily wastes into the sea. They chose 1975 as their target date, and pledged in any case to stop such spills entirely by 1980.

The problem is perhaps more difficult than it looks. It is not only a matter of costs, though the necessary modifications in tankers, terminals, and navigation aids may increase the cost of oil significantly. But considerable technical difficulties are also involved.

The major problem is that tanker crews, having delivered their cargo of oil, must clean their tanks of the oil that could not be pumped out in order to prevent a risk of explosion. Since the tankers are designed to sail with a full cargo, the usual procedure is to wash down the tanks with sea water, collect that wash water in one of the tanks, and refill the empty tanks with sea-water as ballast. During the voyage the slops in the collecting tank are allowed to separate into oil and water layers. Near the end of the voyage, the ballast and the water in the slop tank are pumped overboard, leaving the slop oil to become part of the next cargo.

This process, however, cannot be carried out perfectly and thus much oil goes into the sea. To overcome this difficulty, tankers would have to be fitted with special ballast tanks, which would only contain sea water, and slops could be pumped into disposal systems on shore.

There is no agreement yet, however, about the design of tankers and terminals to ensure clean-ballast operation. Also, little is known of the behaviour of petroleum products in the sea. Finally, methods of removing oil or of making it inoffensive are still in an early stage of development. Nevertheless, the experts at the Oil Spills Conference believed that none of these problems was insuperable, provided the necessary resolve and effort was forthcoming. And the resolve was provided by the Foreign Ministers.

The Ministers also committed their countries to work urgently to minimise the risk and consequences of accidental spills of oil ; to press for early implementation of other international agreements on pollution of the sea by oil ; and to accelerate research which could help overcome the problem.

Within the NATO nations are most of the industrial firms which process and market the world's oil, plus most of the heavy consumers. Political and military agreements in NATO have tended in the past to be taken seriously by the member countries. With time, it is likely that CCMS action to deal with oil spills will significantly improve the quality of sea water, marine life, and beaches. The Chairman of CCMS put it this way :

> The NATO oil spills agreement really implies great efforts, great sums of money and a time limit, and I think it is a good sign that the NATO nations have shown the way to other nations as an example of sacrificing something for the good of the environment.

The Oil Spills Conference also demonstrated another virtue of CCMS, i.e., the possibility of organizing a high-level conference rapidly, gathering some of the world's best experts in a given field, and achieving multi-governmental commitment to action — all within six months.

Other Forms of Water Pollution

Belgium, as a "pilot country", is also investigating other forms of sea water pollution. A major source of her concern stems from an alarming recent increase in contamination of the North Sea. Belgium's fisheries are important and her littoral now consists almost entirely of ocean resorts and beaches whose pollution could cause a major falling-off in the tourist industry. France, a neighbour which shares this concern, is a "co-pilot" in the open waters project, as are two other seafaring nations, Portugal and Canada.

Part of the ocean pollution problem is the lack of a convincing scientific case to put before governments that will persuade them that the effort is worth the cost. A recent Belgian report to CCMS states:

> At the present time, we do not know exactly the level of pollution in the sea, nor do we know precisely to what level of purity we ought to restore the sea. We do not know exactly what purification measures ought to be undertaken. And finally, we know only very imperfectly the precise influence of the various pollutants discharged into the sea on the ecology of the marine environmeni.

With the help of several other NATO allies (the United Kingdom, Italy and the United States) Belgium is constructing a mathematical model of the North Sea, to culminate in a cost-benefit analysis linked to the problems om administration and legislation.

As her contribution to the open waters pollution problem, France is studying the legislative problems of the use of the seas.

As fresh water is also a matter of concern for the NATO countries, Canada has agreed to pilot a project with a general goal which is :

> To identify, test, demonstrate and, where appropriate, recommend to member countries through the CCMS the elements, mechanisms and instruments for effective inland water quality management in an interjurisdictional setting.

> As to method, it is hoped to treat as many of these elements, mechanisms and instruments as possible within a three-year time period, the experience and resources of co-operating nations and the available resources of the Alliance.

The geographic focus of the Canadian effort will be the St. John River, which rises in the American State of Maine and flows through New Brunswick to the Bay of Fundy. Both the American and Canadian federal governments, as well as the governments of the Province of New Brunswick and the State of Maine, will be involved. In presenting its plans to CCMS, the Canadian Government stated :

> Canada is prepared to provide for full international review of the effectiveness of the programme.

Also, the Canadians put their finger on a delicate point :

> The final success of the (pilot project) on Inland Water Pollution will depend in very large measure on the degree to which pilot and co-pilot countries can move beyond traditional meetings of experts and find new methods to achieve effective participation among specialists from different countries.

This illustrates the growing difficulty, in the technological age, of relating specialised knowledge and government structures to the solution of precise problems. From a broader angle, the CCMS project chosen by the Federal Republic of Germany is addressed to this same important question.

The end result ? Canada, and her co-pilots, France, Belgium and the United States, hope to work out a basic concept and procedure for water basin management, involving natural and social scientists, planners, and citizenry, which could be used by any government in working out a plan to purify its inland waters.

The cause of oil-free seas, clean coastal waters, and pure rivers may well be advanced through CCMS efforts. But there are still more environmental issues on NATO's agenda. The CCMS programme also addresses itself to the goal of pollution-free air, with the United States as pilot country and West Germany and Turkey as co-pilots.

The Clean Engine

With more than 85 million motor vehicles on its high-ways, the United States has had to face first a massive onslaught of exhaust pollutants. Some cities, such as Los Angeles, face serious air pollution crises brought on by the ubiquitous automobile. Europe is catching up fast ; the present growth rate of the vehicle population (1971) is now twice that of the United States and Canada.

Very recently, the search for an effective means of combat has turned to the possibility of developing a "clean engine" — one which would provide virtually pollution-free power. In 1970, the US Federal Government began a two-pronged programme to develop, in co-operation with private industry, a workable "clean engine".

To explain its efforts and enlist the help of other countries, the United States called a conference in the Dutch city of Eindhoven in February 1971, to which any interested party was invited. Government and industry representatives from the Netherlands. Belgium, Canada, Denmark, France, Germany, Great Britain, Italy, Turkey and the United States took part, as well as two non-NATO members, Japan and Sweden. The OECD and the EEC also took part.

A series of technical papers were put forward, including a Japanese account of progress towards an electric power system, a German report on gas turbines, and a Dutch presentation of the Stirling hot-air engine, in development at Philips. The new Dutch air pollution control law was also discussed.

In keeping with the CCMS policy of open information, all technical papers presented at the conference were released to the press and public.

The purpose of the Eindhoven "clean engine" meeting ? To try to accelerate the exchange of technology so that a pollution-free car will come about faster than if each country had been left on its own ; to stimulate the Europeans to treat the problem with the same urgency as the Americans ; and to give the European automotive industry plenty of lead-time for complying with new US pollution regulations.

Here is CCMS at work as a catalyst, concentrating concern on an important problem.

Air Pollution Control

With NATO's help, Frankfurt, Ankara, and St. Louis, Mo. may clean up their air a little faster.

The Frankfurt region is large, with an advanced state of multicentre urbanisation and a wide variety of dispersed heavy industry. Frankfurt weather conditions are highly variable.

St. Louis spans the Mississipi River and the two States of Illinois and Missouri ; the problems inherent in control by more than one political jurisdiction must be dealt with, along with an industrial-urban area similar in size and scope to that of Frankfurt. Motor vehicle pollution is especially heavy.

Ankara's problem is that of air polluted heavily by lignite burning stoves and furnaces in a concentrated urban area with low winter temperatures.

Under leadership of the United States as pilot, and with Turkey and the Federal German Republic as co-pilots, existing knowledge will be pulled together and applied as quickly as possible to the air pollution problems — each different — of the three model cities. The quality of the air is being evaluated, criteria for quality are being set up, and the technology available to control air pollution is under assessment. Again, the use of mathematical models is providing a short-cut.

The aim is to prod all the NATO governments to systematically assess their air pollution problems, adopt common standards where possible, and structure their control agencies to carry out aggressive effective programmes. Air quality standards and procedures will be as comprehensive as possible, to facilitate their use by any country in the world.

The Experimental Safety Vehicle

The total number of servicemen who died on the UN side in the Korean War (118,515) was only slightly greater than the number of traffic deaths (111,000) in all NATO countries in one recent year (1965-66). Either loss of life — through war, or mindless slaughter on the highways — is needless, and more than modern governments or peoples can accept with complacency.

In the United States, highway injuries exceed by nearly 10 times all violent criminal acts combined, including homicides, armed robbery, rape, riot and assault.

Any number of statistical indicators suggest that the problem of road safety is at least as serious — if not more so — in Europe. In 1966-67, for example, the traffic death rate per 100 million miles travelled in the United States was 5.6, compared to 7.0 in Britain, 8.0 in Norway, 9.7 in Denmark, 12.1 in Italy, 13.3 in West Germany, 13.3 in France and 16.1 in the Netherlands.

It is not surprising that the United States Government is attaching the problem of exhaust pollution along wih that of vehicle safety ; the "clean car" of 1975 will also have to be a "safe car". Tough new US regulations will force manufacturers to correct safety-related defects in their cars ; will enforce uniform standards for driver education and licensing, motor vehicle inspection, alcohol and driving safety among the States ; and will require that all new motor vehicles meet unprecedented standards of safety performance.

The United States is piloting a CCMS project on road safety, with priority attention to the "Experimental Safety Vehicle" (ESV). If a truly "safe car" could be introduced generally, road injury rates might be cut dramatically. The intention is to develop an automobile which would prevent casualties even after a collision at 50 miles per hour.

Swift progress towards an ESV has been made.

The first international ESV conference, to exchange technical data related to the design specifications for a safe car, was held in Paris in January 1971. Government and industry from the principal NATO countries attended, plus representatives from Sweden and Japan. Subsequently, a division of labour in Europe for research and development on the safe car was agreed on under a "European Intergovernmental Committee on ESV".

Prior to commencing the CCMS work, the United States was well along on the design for a 4000-pound ESV. Within the NATO framework, there is already a bi-lateral American agreement with West Germany and prospects for similar ones with Italy, France and Britain to speed ESV development work. A US-Japanese agreement has also been signed. The Germans and Japanese have both completed their study of the design specifications for a 2000-pound ESV (more suited to roads and tastes outside North America).

With co-ordinated effort, it seems likely that a successful safe car, incorporating such features as improved safety belts, air bags under dashboards which inflate instantly on collision, and safer placement of engines, could be travelling the highways in a relatively short time.

Other Aspects of Road Safety

There are other ways to improve Road Safety, and
CCMS is now exploring most of them.

Canada is doing a study of alcohol and driving, which
could lead to stricter laws and better enforcement in
NATO countries.

Still more needs to be known about the causes of
accidents ; therefore the Netherlands Government is
chairing a panel of representatives from countries
carrying out investigations of crashes to see what
can be learned and shared. Teams from NATO countries are now participating frequently in accident
investigation training courses in the United States.

The Federal German Government has taken the lead
in the effort to pull together the best experience on
the periodic inspection of motor vehicles.

A study on road hazards is underway by the French
Government, while the Belgians are considering the
problem of pedestrian safety.

The Italian Government is in charge of work on emergency medical services to deal with road accidents.
In this respect, it is interesting to note a sentence
in the minutes of a recent meeting of CCMS :

> The United States found itself considerably behind
> other nations such as Italy in (the organization of emer-
> gency medical response systems) and was keen to
> obtain information in order to improve its national prac-
> tices.

Later in the meeting, the Italian delegate invited
representatives of the United States to visit Italy and
observe the emergency medical services at firsthand.
This illustrates an important principle of the entire
CCMS effort : it assumes — and practice has already
borne this out — that no nation can claim to-day
a full understanding of all the intricate factors that
go to make up the complex of urgent environmental

issues. No nation, not even the largest, has a monopoly on the best practices to combat environmental deterioration. And if the NATO nations work hard and fast to share whatever knowledge each of them possesses with respect to the major aspects of the crisis, then jointly, and overall, their countermeasures are bound to improve the situation much more rapidly than if each continued to work in isolation.

In this context, the Road Safety Project is particularly interesting. The field has suffered immeasurably because of a continuing record of piecemeal approaches, both within and among countries. The NATO project is seen as a first step, directed at priority problems, in what is to-day known as a "systems approach" to the whole question of road accident reduction. The ultimate goal of the pilot study is to organize all road safety information available in all member nations within the context of a rational framework. In a real sense, this study could ultimately prove to be a "pilot of pilots".

Work Satisfaction in a Technological Era

CCMS does not restrict itself to physical problems of the environment, such as pollution and road safety, but is turning its attention also to social questions of a broad nature. "The Challenges of Modern Society", as an overall title for the NATO programme, indeed implies a wide range of problems.

The United Kingdom chose to deal, as pilot country, with the question of motivation and work satisfaction. Despite the many and obvious benefits brought to man by modern technology, there are also nagging fears in many countries that on balance technology "dehumanizes" work. People fear that personal human values will be overshadowed by technical and administrative needs. The British team reasons that perhaps some of the scientific methods and acumen which have made technology such a formidable force should be applied to the theme of human work. Otherwise, if major and concentrated attention is not given to this complicated problem — common to all advanced societies — both efficiency and work satisfaction could decline rapidly, with untold consequences for our civilisation.

The British pilot study is developed around two main lines of thought :

1. The influence of the conditions of work upon the carrying out of the work ; and

2. An appraisal of experiments in job enrichment and enlargement presently underway in industry in various countries.

Disaster Assistance

Man has learned, by applying science and technology, to make nature perform at his command. But despite great advances in clothing and housing man, and keeping him warm and comfortable, the human species is still prey to floods, earthquakes, forest fires, cyclones and other natural disasters. CCMS, with the United States as pilot nation and Italy and Turkey as co-pilots, has taken up the challenge in this field. Several studies are under way which could help mitigate the effects of disasters and, conceivably, lead to ways of controlling or even preventing some of them.

The effectiveness of the response to human suffering in a great flood or earthquake depends in part on swift and accurate communications. NATO probably possesses the most efficient communications network in the world, covering its member countries and based on the most modern systems of satellite transmission. This network, centralized on the Brussels civil headquarters and NATO's military commands, is used to insure constant readiness of the Alliance's forces and to facilitate swift exchanges of political and diplomatic messages between the Allies. There is no reason why this communications system cannot be put at the disposal of national authorities in the event of, say, a flood in Italy or an earthquake in Turkey.

Some years ago, NATO developed a plan for common action in the event of a natural disaster in one of its member countries. This is now being updated, and includes possibilities for co-operation with the International Red Cross. The Italians are working particularly on a plan for the quick dispatch of helicopters, advance agreements with hospitals, and other forms of emergency medical services. One of the principles of CCMS is that the results of its work will be open to all countries ; in the case of disaster relief, the UN and its members all stand to profit from new techniques developed by NATO.

At the present stage, however, national disaster plans may be even more important than international ones, so a great deal of CCMS emphasis is being put on an exchange of information and experience which can improve the readiness of individual NATO members. For example, NATO documents are now being circulated with such headings as "Netherlands Military Experience in Rendering Emergency Assistance to other Countries", or "Detailed Report by Italy on its National Disaster Experience".

Is it possible to predict flash floods ? This is only one of the questions concerning floods now under CCMS review. Also being considered are a NATO Disaster Information Centre, advance arrangements to co-ordinate international assistance in time of flooding, the development of automated hydrologic networks, and the improvement of lower atmospheric forecasting.

Some NATO countries are subject to frequent — and occasionally disastrous — earthquakes. A workshop on earthquake hazard reduction was sponsored by CCMS at San Francisco, a particularly vulnerable point on the "Rim of Fire" which circles the edge of the Pacific. Turkey has a particular hand in the continuation of this project, which involves communicators, civil servants, scientists, and technicians in such exercises as "earthquake engineering", an inquiry into the behaviour of tall buildings during the Caracas Earthquake of 1967, and seismic studies on concrete dam models.

Scientific Knowledge and Decision-Making

In the category of sociological questions, with the broadest kind of implications for modern societies, is another CCMS project undertaken by the Federal Republic of Germany.

There is today literally a flood of knowledge coming out of universities and scientific institutes. Much of it could be immediately useful to society, yet only a small fraction is actually known to or employed by governments. In part, the reason lies in the sheer magnitude of the flood, in part in the complexity of modern society itself.

The problem, as a German Government paper puts it, "is how to achieve co-operation between politics and science".

The German pilot team is studying the specific subjects under consideration in other CCMS projects as examples of how existing scientific and technical knowledge is — or is not — applied to governmental decision-making.

Environment and the Strategy of Regional Development

All the CCMS projects and programmes so far described might be classified as "sector" or "vertical" approaches to environmental problems. Such an approach makes it easier to reach conclusions of practical use to policy-makers, but it fails to impart an understanding of what is meant by the environment as a whole. Consequently the French Government has chosen to pilot a CCMS study devoted to the interconnection between environmental problems in the framework of regional development.

The French project examines the relative efficiency of regional and local institutions in dealing with environmental policy, and the relationship between environment and territorial, economic and social development. There is also a case study in contrasting geographic sites, i.e., a rapidly industrialising area next to a protected natural reserve.

As a co-pilot in the regional development project, the United Kingdom is studying the application of government at various levels. The United States, as a participating country, is investigating possibilities of introducing new kinds of governmental institutions to manage environmental problems, especially air pollution.

Cities

CCMS collaborated in a United States conference of Mayors and Local Authorities at Indianapolis (25th-28th May, 1971), in which other international organizations and many mayors and other senior officials from Europe and Canada took part. During the conference — the theme of which was "Innovation in the Cities" — new approaches were discussed to problems such as Environment, Recreation, Housing, Transportation, Public Health and Safety, Local Government Organization, Planning and Development, Fiscal Resources.

The Misuse of Drugs

Perhaps one of the most formidable challenges facing modern society is the alarming and increasingly widespread use of dangerous and habit-forming drugs. CCMS has held a series of meetings on the subject and urged NATO members to support strongly the drug control measures undertaken by other international bodies (notably the United Nations). There is not, however, a pilot project in this field.

Environmental Fellowships

In December 1970 the North Atlantic Council adopted the CCMS proposal for a fellowship programme designed to stimulate the study of the problems of public policy in relation to the natural and social environment. The programme is established on an experimental basis and the number of fellows will be limited to five for the first year.

WHY NATO ?

NATO is more than a military alliance. It is an alliance for the stability of its member nations.

Professor Gunnar Randers, Assistant Secretary General of NATO for Scientific Affairs.

The very fact that this Committee has been created shows that for us, security depends as much on the vitality of our societies as it does on the strength of our armies.

Professor Ralf Dahrendorf (Federal German Republic) at the first meeting of CCMS.

THE reader has now had spread before him the full range of NATO's present concerns in the environmental field. Yet it would be only natural if a question were to remain in his mind : Is it not curious that the North Atlantic Treaty Organization, set up originally for the defence of Western Europe and North America, should involve itself in social and ecological questions ?

This chapter seeks to provide an answer, and to describe the rationale behind CCMS and its working methods. It also explains NATO's efforts to avoid duplication of what others are doing, and to coordinate its work in the environmental field with that of other international organizations.

Why should NATO be doing this kind of a job ?

In April 1969, when President Nixon proposed the CCMS idea on NATO's twentieth birthday, he is said to have had three basic propositions in mind :

1. That there existed within the nations of the... Alliance a powerful. if still somewhat latent, concern with the deterioration, indeed, in many instances, the degrad-

ation, of the national environments under the impact of technologically based industrialisation. Correspondingly, that there existed an equally widespread conviction that the opportunities provided by that same technology to create a significantly more fulfilling and meaningful social environment had only begun to be realised;

2. That there was already in existence a considerable body of technical knowledge that, if applied with sufficient vigour and purpose, would enable industrial societies to halt and to reverse the degradation of the natural environment, and also that the methodologies of contemporary social enquiry offered considerable possibilities for social advances; and

3. That NATO countries, in the course of two decades of military alliance and political consultation, had acquired the governmental skills which would enable them to act in concert with respect to those aspects of the natural and social environment which either required international action or which might best respond to a multinational effort.

In determining whether or not NATO has a role in environmental protection, the President's third point is the heart of the matter. One must begin by understanding what NATO is and how it works.

To link together in peacetime alliance the human and material resources of fifteen nations, spanning a sizeable portion of the earth's surface, is no mean achievement. Under modern conditions, it has meant that NATO had to organize multinational military commands and training systems, build supply depots and airfields all over Europe, construct new roads and pipelines from the North Cape to Anatolia, put up a vast communications and air-warning network, and create harmonized logistical and armament systems for its forces. All of this — and much more — was accomplished in an incredibly brief span of time.

NATO, recognizing the unprecedented requirements of modern war, also went behind the panoply and organization to consider what science could provide for technology to develop over the long term. This led to a considerable effort to support the basic as well as applied sciences, and to create manifold inter-Allied committees, working groups, and research and development agencies.

NATO, almost uniquely among international organizations, is geared to achieving physical results, quickly. Therefore, our first answer to the question, Why NATO ? is :

To the extent that the problem of creating a better environment for man is a question of the transfer and application of technology, NATO has impressive qualifications.

Next, NATO is an action-orientated organization.

The CCMS programme, as conceived, is aimed at stimulating governments to *act* on environmental issues.

The problems of diplomacy, defence, and high politics with which NATO is accustomed to deal usually call for decisions or other action by governments or international authorities. Over the years, NATO has developed an impressive capability to sift through major problems in multinational teams, to marshall facts from highly diverse sources, and to hammer out agreements and plans for action between governments representing highly individualised peoples and political systems.

So our second answer to Why NATO ? is :

Because NATO can work fast, and is geared to action.

The Alliance's next qualification can perhaps be best understood by beginning with a quote from Dr. Moynihan, who said at the first CCMS meeting : "We bring this initiative to NATO, this issue of the environment, because we regard it as fundamentally serious."

Collective security is a serious business. When the Allies brought NATO into being, they were seeking

34

to insure their survival. As the maintenance of a firm defence posture over years has favoured a hopeful, if still small, lessening of tension in relations with the East, NATO's diplomatic tasks and talents have grown. But the seriousness of every undertaking of the Alliance remains constant. Because of this, member governments tend to listen when the North Atlantic Council, composed of Ministers — or more regularly, of their high-level Permanent Representatives in continual session in Brussels — address them.

A third answer to Why NATO ? is thus :

NATO is the political expression of the most vital ties between Europe and North America, and thus well-suited to a common task which requires sensitivity, mutual understanding, and a capacity for international teamwork.

Shining like a small precious stone in an otherwise routine Canadian Government paper on the CCMS Inland Water Pollution Project is the following paragraph :

> Nations throughout history have found it necessary to forge alliances as protection from external aggression. There is no precedent in history for the environmental and ecological decay and the attendant social disruption that is now perhaps the greatest threat to the established order in developed countries. New alliances for co-operation must be formed to provide the same co-operative effort against the threat of environmental decay.

NATO is an old alliance, ready to be used for these fresh purposes.

International Duplication and Co-ordination

Cleaning up the global environment and up-dating modern society are huge tasks. And they appear, at least to most people, relatively new. It is only very recently that these have come to be seen as proper subjects for international organizations.

The United Nations, UNESCO, the World Health Organization, the Food and Agriculture Organization, the UN's Economic Commission for Europe, the Organization for Economic Co-operation and Development, the Council of Europe, the European Communities, and still other international and regional bodies have lately addressed themselves to one or more aspects of the environmental crisis.

If NATO joins this list, is there not danger of duplication? Is yet another international organization needed in this field?

Our answers to the question Why NATO? help to explain why there is a special role for the Alliance. But there is more to be said.

Still a fourth answer to our question, therefore, is :

Because NATO is able to command the attention and response of governments at a high level.

Some critics have asserted that, "as NATO is a military organization", it should have no role in non-military fields. To see the Alliance as simply a military organization is to misunderstand fundamentally its nature. The North Atlantic Alliance came into being as a mutual defence organization, and defence remains its priority task. But from the beginning, NATO was a *political* organization, intended for a wide variety of purposes. Article 2 of the North Atlantic Treaty provided the broad legal and philosophical framework. Alongside its role in creating a common defence arm for the Atlantic Community, the Alliance has developed an impressive capability in the field of foreign policy. And its activities in scientific economic and cultural co-operation are not negligible.

36

Another answer, then, is this :

The Alliance, much more than just a military organization, has a charter and a history which fit it for a wide variety of tasks.

Finally, there is the Alliance's position as a vital hinge in the US-European relationship. Western Europe and North America share several fundamental interests : security from aggression, the prosperity of an interdependent trans-Atlantic economy, the provision of effective aid to the Third World, and the development of a stable world peace system. The Alliance represents the political institutionalisation of these vital interests and of a common set of ideals and political traditions, the heart of a nascent community. It is therefore eminently appropriate that the Alliance take on the defence of still another set of common interests : the preservation and improvement of the quality of life in Western society.

It is true that a great deal of the environmental effort must involve long-range study and research, often basic scientific research. In the environmental and social fields, this kind of research is best left to other international organizations. But to mount an effective attack will also require international *action,* and this NATO has shown itself well-qualified to bring about.

Moreover, the international environmental jobs that need doing are many and varied ; most are not yet even properly understood. For the next few years at least, there is a strong argument for encouraging a fairly large number of international bodies to explore and experiment with a wide variety of approaches. Then, as time goes on, the experience of NATO and other organizations can be analysed and a rational long-range scheme drawn up, hopefully on a global basis. But it is still far too early to do this.

With respect to duplication, several things can be said :

1. Most overlapping can be avoided, if the heads of international and regional organizations will consult one another and secretariats will share advance plans and proposals. In this respect, all of NATO's CCMS work is entirely open to other international organizations. The Secretary General and his chief deputies meet often with those of other bodies to consult and concert their efforts. Also, it has become common practice for the various organizations to send observers to one another's conferences.

2. There *is* a problem, especially for small countries, in that environmental specialists are still few. If a country belongs to several international bodies, all dealing with ecological questions, the specialists need to keep their bags packed ; and work at home may suffer. NATO's unique "pilot country" method* of dealing with CCMS projects, however, minimises this, as the work is done less in international meetings and more by individual member countries at their home base. NATO countries other than the "pilot" participate in a given CCMS project only if they feel able.

3. Duplication is not always a bad thing. If, for example, one wants to measure the pollution in the air over a particular area of Western Europe, this might be done by country "A". But it would be a good thing if it were also measured by Country "B", because there is always the risk, in scientific work of this sort, of bias or some other element that gives rise to doubt. To take a second case : If, for example, the respective machinery of both OECD and NATO were put to work on the same environmental topic, this would not necessarily result in waste. If the conclusions of both organizations were different, one would of course want to know why. And in getting the answer, new knowledge might result. If the conclusions were the same, then there could be double pressure for action.

* For full description of the pilot country method see page 40.

The real worry today is not that too much is being done about the environment, but too little. At the present, there are not too many but too few international and regional organizations to undertake a wide variety of pressing tasks.

To end this discussion aimed at fitting NATO's environmental activities into a broader international pattern, one should perhaps ponder the question of whether the environmental crisis is not so totally global that only bodies with universal (or near-universal) membership, such as the UN, should concern themselves with it.

Part of the answer is that it is much more difficult to get a consensus in favour of meaningful action when the forum is global, than if membership is restricted to more like-minded countries, as in regional organizations such as the Council of Europe or NATO. It is the advanced countries who are most conscious of the environmental crisis and its attendant social revolution ; it therefore seems fitting that they forge ahead to investigate the problems and work out at least some tentative solutions. Whatever results are achieved can be laid before the world community for such action as it is able and willing to take.

A good example of this is the CCMS action on oil spills : the NATO countries account for 80 % of all transported oil. An agreement among them is clearly a giant step towards solving the global problem.

The other part of the answer is that some environmental problems are peculiar to the advanced countries. Neither Burma nor Guinea nor Bolivia, for example, are yet plagued by auto exhaust fumes or a serious level of road accidents. So it is up to the advanced countries, through their own fora — such as OECD and NATO — to deal now with their own problems.

CCMS Concepts and Methods

Three concepts are pivotal :
— the pilot country idea ;
— the orientation towards action, rather than research ;
— the policy of open publicity.

The pilot country concept is indeed new and original.
It grew out of experience in NATO and other international organizations with the "rapporteur country"
method of seeing a particular project or study
through. Rapporteur countries, however, are not res-
ponsible for getting action, nor are they expected to
pay for the studies. And under this system, the secretariats of international organizations are heavily involved.

In the *pilot country* method, one country takes over
responsibility for a project which CCMS had decided
is worth doing. The pilot country plans the study, pays
for it, prepares all the necessary reports, and — if it
can — tries to see that action ensues.

Not only has this avoided an enlargement of the
NATO international secretariat and budget, but it has
insured that the work is properly motivated : a country volunteers as a pilot only if it has serious inten-
tions to do the work well.

Under the pilot country method, another member
country can be a "co-pilot" if it wants to make a
significant contribution, and any other member is
equally welcome if its interest and capabilities fall
short of a desire for formal association, yet it still
wishes to participate at any level.

The *action-orientation* concept, as suggested earlier,
has grown too out of NATO's experience. Research
takes time and money ; CCMS wants to collect and

boil down existing research (actually a vast amount of it is available) with respect to a given problem, lay facts and recommendations before the members, and stimulate them to act.

Each pilot project will have a finite lifetime, with the goal of translating largely existing knowledge into practical application in a reasonable time, specifically by the creation of national legislation.

Both these concepts — the pilot country and action-orientation — have their drawbacks. For example, it may be asked whether the eight projects presently in progress necessarily encompass the most important problems facing Society ; probably they do not. Pragmatically they are the ones which countries have offered to lead, and presumably they are those which have likelihood of some reasonable progress or success.

There is also the possible danger that CCMS methods may lead to the "quick technological fix" — short-term solutions which could conceivably result in new, unforeseen problems. This danger however must be balanced against the need to find workable — if not necessarily perfect — solutions to some crisis problems (such as auto-accidents) quickly. One must also have some faith in the quality of the work being done, which the NATO method of scrutiny by fifteen governments and qualified experts helps to insure.

The third CCMS concept — *open publicity* — is a radical departure for NATO. Of necessity, much of its work in the past has had to be done in secret, as it directly affected the security of every member.

Even though the subjects dealt with by CCMS, in-directly but in the deepest sense, affect security too, they are of an entirely different sort. Social and environmental issues are matters of global concern and they are most imperfectly understood ; hence everyone, including potential enemies of the Alliance, can only gain if the results of CCMS studies are made widely available, without limitations.

No CCMS papers bear security restrictions. The press has been invited to meetings of the Committee on the Challenges of Modern Society. All other intergovernmental organizations may be permitted to send observers to any CCMS activity. And there is a liberal policy with respect to other outside observers in CCMS-sponsored meetings ; the United States, for example, has invited the USSR, as well as other countries not in NATO, to attend meetings concerned with its pilot projects. Finally, the North Atlantic Council will make available the results of all CCMS studies to other international organizations and to any country, anywhere.

Still another comment needs to be made about the CCMS concept. There is no intention of setting up NATO as an international policing or enforcement body. The goal is rather to distil available knowledge and suggest to governments practical steps for executive action, national legislation, public education, and the like. The rationale is that intensive study of a given environmental problem, and subsequent review by both substantive and political experts, will result in practical and realistic suggestions for action. National authorities, in the last resort, will have responsibility for putting them into effect.

Finally, the CCMS programme can perhaps be best understood if one reflects on the name — Committee on the Challenges of Modern Society. In the initial stages, thought was given to use of the world "environment" in the title, but this was rejected in favour of the broader wording. As it now stands, this reflects the wish of the NATO countries to include all problems, whether social, technological or scientific, which derive directly or indirectly from technological development.

42

THE FUTURE OF CCMS

Results Already

IMPORTANT steps have been taken through CCMS to bring about a clean, safe motorcar. And it is more than likely that oil spills in the oceans will diminish sooner because of the action that has been initiated in CCMS.

Perhaps the most important result of CCMS so far has been the action of several of the member countries who have suddenly found it essential to create organizational structures to deal with environmental problems. New government departments, cabinet-level co-ordinating committees, and specialized agencies have sprung up, almost literally over the whole North Atlantic area.

More than this, in specific terms, it is too early to claim for CCMS, although all studies now under way contain the promise of significant advances for all of mankind, not just the NATO sponsors. One can say, however, that less than a year after its creation, CCMS had become an important forum for NATO members to bring to each other's attention critical environmental problems, and that it had begun to exercise a significant function as a catalyst for action.

What of the future ?

First, one can envision a kind of trade in ideas springing up among the Allies. The law of comparative advantage can come into effect : as one nation learns to cope with this problem, another with that, the ability can be exchanged to the benefit of both. To some extent this already takes place ; a trans-Atlantic society is willy-nilly developing and two decades of the Atlantic Alliance has accelerated the process. But the great fact of the age is that time is short, and governments must get about their business with far greater urgency and effectiveness than before. CCMS can smooth the way for a rational, even massive, interchange of experience.

One can also reasonably expect that the CCMS process will bring breakthroughs in methodology ; for example, once a mathematical model has been successfully developed, as in the Belgian North Sea Pollution project or the Ankara Air Pollution Study, it could be adapted for use in areas other than that for which it had originally been conceived. In effect, as Dr. Moynihan once pointed out at a CCMS meeting, CCMS in this way is pioneering the development of "machine-tools" — techniques and models which may subsequently be put to more general use.

Still another expectation : one can probably anticipate that CCMS activities, although geared to action rather than research, will nevertheless serve to stimulate a much greater effort to get the necessary scientific research done. This is because inevitably, studies of the CCMS sort expose the gaping holes in our scientific knowledge about the environment. The research will not be done in NATO or under its aegis, but NATO may, indirectly, have helped to see that it got done by somebody else.

Finally, there is hope that in the long run, recommendations flowing out of the CCMS projects will result in internationally agreed standards for the environment ; the Air Pollution Project is a step in this direction. It is possible that eventually "NATO Codes of Best Practice" and hopefully at some point "UN Codes" can be established. Although in the beginning there may not be an international authority to enforce them,

44

that too could come some day. In this respect, the NATO Oil Spills Agreement may, as a kind of rude prototype, foreshadow things to come.

The North Atlantic Alliance cannot alone resolve the world environmental crisis ; it is far too big an under-taking. But there is a conviction around the North Atlantic Council table that NATO has an important contribution to make in helping to provide a more decent environment and lives of quality for future generations.

APPENDIX

A CCMS CHRONOLOGY

1969

10 April	President Nixon proposes a "Third Dimension" for NATO — a programme on the challenges of modern society.
11 April	Foreign Ministers of the allied countries, in a press communique, announce that NATO will study the idea.
14 May	Council of Permanent Representatives, in Brussels, sets up a Preparatory Committee to find out how the Alliance could make a useful contribution.
6 November	North Atlantic Council decides to create the Committee on the Challenges of Modern Society (CCMS).
8 December	First Plenary Meeting of CCMS.

1970

28 January	North Atlantic Council accepts first CCMS pilot projects.
9-12 March	Meeting of 40 Experts on Air Pollution Project in Ankara.
13-14 April	Second Plenary Meeting of CCMS.
11-12 May	Workshop in Detroit of leading auto manufacturers (including Japan) to exchange latest technology on auto safety devices (Road Safety Project).
19-20 October	Third Plenary Meeting of CCMS.
23 October	Conference in Venice on Flood Control and Relief (Disaster Relief Project).
2-6 November	Oil Spills Conference in Brussels (Open Waters Pollution).

1971

25-27 January	Conference on the Experimental Safety Vehicle (ESV) in Paris (Road Safety Project).
23-25 February	" Clean Engine " Conference in Eindhoven (Air Pollution Project).

1-3 March	Organization Meeting for Inland Water Pollution Project, Brussels.
19-20 April	Fourth Plenary Meeting of CCMS.
22-23 April	Organization Meeting, Pilot Project on Environment and Regional Development.
18-25 May	Conference on Earthquakes, San Francisco (Disaster Relief Project).
26-28 May	Conference on Cities, Indianapolis.